F

ESC

OXFORD BOOKWORMS
Series Editor: Tricia Hedge

For a full list of titles in all the Oxford Bookworms series,
please refer to the *Oxford English* catalogue.

~ Black Series ~

Titles available include:

~Stage 1 (400 headwords)
*The Elephant Man *Tim Vicary*
*The Monkey's Paw *W.W.Jacobs*
Under the Moon *Rowena Akinyemi*
*The Phantom of the Opera *Jennifer Bassett*

~Stage 2 (700 headwords)
*Sherlock Holmes Short Stories
 Sir Arthur Conan Doyle
*Voodoo Island *Michael Duckworth*
*New Yorkers *O.Henry* (short stories)

~Stage 3 (1000 headwords)
*Skyjack! *Tim Vicary*
Love Story *Erich Segal*
Tooth and Claw *Saki* (short stories)
Wyatt's Hurricane *Desmond Bagley*

~Stage 4 (1400 headwords)
*The Hound of the Baskervilles
 Sir Arthur Conan Doyle
*Three Men in a Boat *Jerome K. Jerome*
The Big Sleep *Raymond Chandler*

~Stage 5 (1800 headwords)
*Ghost Stories *retold by Rosemary Border*
The Dead of Jericho *Colin Dexter*
*Wuthering Heights *Emily Brontë*
I, Robot *Isaac Asimov* (short stories)

~Stage 6 (2500 headwords)
*Tess of the d'Urbervilles *Thomas Hardy*
Cry Freedom *John Briley*
Meteor *John Wyndham* (short stories)
Deadheads *Reginald Hill*

Many other titles available, both classic and modern.
**Cassettes available for these titles.*

~ Green Series ~

Adaptations of classic and modern stories for younger readers.
Titles available include:

~Stage 2 (700 headwords)
*Robinson Crusoe *Daniel Defoe*
*Alice's Adventures in Wonderland *Lewis Carroll*
Too Old to Rock and Roll *Jan Mark* (short stories)

~Stage 3 (1000 headwords)
*The Prisoner of Zenda *Anthony Hope*
*The Secret Garden *Frances Hodgson Burnett*
On the Edge *Gillian Cross*

~Stage 4 (1400 headwords)
*Treasure Island *Robert Louis Stevenson*
*Gulliver's Travels *Jonathan Swift*
A Tale of Two Cities *Charles Dickens*
The Silver Sword *Ian Serraillier*

OXFORD BOOKWORMS COLLECTION

Fiction by well-known authors, both classic and modern.
Texts are not abridged or simplified in any way. Titles available include:

From the Cradle to the Grave
 (short stories by *Saki, Evelyn Waugh, Roald Dahl,*
 Susan Hill, Somerset Maugham, H. E. Bates,
 Frank Sargeson, Raymond Carver)

Crime Never Pays
 (short stories by *Agatha Christie,*
 Graham Greene, Ruth Rendell, Angela Noel,
 Dorothy L. Sayers, Margery Allingham,
 Sir Arthur Conan Doyle, Patricia Highsmith)

Dead Man's Island

John Escott

OXFORD UNIVERSITY PRESS

Oxford University Press
Walton Street, Oxford OX2 6DP

Oxford New York
Athens Auckland Bangkok Bombay
Calcutta Cape Town Dar es Salaam Delhi
Florence Hong Kong Istanbul Karachi
Kuala Lumpur Madras Madrid Melbourne
Mexico City Nairobi Paris Singapore
Taipei Tokyo Toronto

and associated companies in
Berlin Ibadan

OXFORD and OXFORD ENGLISH
are trade marks of Oxford University Press

ISBN 0 19 421657 8

First published 1991
Sixth impression 1995

No unauthorized photocopying

Illustrated by Alan Marks

Printed in England by Clays Ltd, St Ives plc

Coming to England

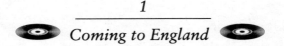

My name is Carol Sanders.

I live in England now, but when I was younger, I lived in Hong Kong. My father was a businessman there and my mother worked as a secretary. We lived in Hong Kong for seven years.

I was happy at school, with lots of friends, and we had a good time. I liked pop music – the Rolling Stones, David Bowie and Jake Rosso were my favourites.

Jake Rosso was my favourite singer. He died in a car accident the year I left school, but I listened to his pop records all the time. I had hundreds of pictures and photos of him on my bedroom wall.

Then one day in winter when I was seventeen, things began to go wrong for me.

My father went to Australia on business. I loved him very much and didn't like him going away.

'Come home quickly,' I always said to him.

He was in Australia for two weeks. Then, on the day of his journey home, an aeroplane from Sydney crashed into the sea just south of Hong Kong. Everybody on the plane died.

I heard about the plane crash on television. At first, I did not think about my father. Then I remembered he was flying back from Sydney on that day.

'Oh, no!' I cried.

I telephoned the airport but they did not know the names of all the passengers then.

'Perhaps my father didn't get that plane,' I thought. 'Oh, please! Please!'

My mother was at work and I called her on the telephone. She came home quickly and we went to the airport and waited for news.

Later, we learned my father was on the plane.

'It's not true!' I shouted.

But it was true, and I began to cry.

I was happy in Hong Kong.

I cried for weeks and weeks. I spent many days alone in my room. I was lonely and sad and I wanted to die, too.

I stopped going out with my friends. I didn't want to see other people. I stopped listening to Jake Rosso's records, and took his pictures off my bedroom wall. I didn't listen to music or watch television. Nothing mattered any more.

Then I stopped crying. I stopped feeling sad and began to feel angry.

'Why did it happen to him?' I asked my mother. 'Why do the best people die? Jake Rosso. My father.'

'I . . . I don't know, Carol,' my mother said. She was unhappy, too.

At the time of the plane crash, I was a student at college. I enjoyed the work and college life very much, but after my father's death I stopped doing my work at the college. I began to go out with some new friends. They were different from my other friends, and my mother didn't like them.

'They're bad people, Carol,' she told me. 'They do dangerous things.'

'They're exciting,' I said. 'And I like them.'

I knew she was angry but I didn't care. But then I learned my new friends took drugs, and I began to take drugs, too. It was wrong and stupid, I know that now, but I was unhappy and angry.

The police came to the college to arrest some of the

4

students. They didn't arrest me, but I had to leave the college. It was a bad time.

My mother was very unhappy with me. 'What am I going to do with you, Carol?' she said.

'I'm sorry,' I told her.

'We'll go back to England,' she said. 'You can find a college there. Perhaps you can be happier in England.'

'All right,' I said. 'I want to forget what's happened. I want to forget what I've done and begin a new life, be a new person.'

I knew my mother was angry, but I didn't care.

A month later, we came back to England. We lived in London, in a hotel. It was strange, at first, with all the red buses and everybody speaking English. It was the beginning of the summer, three months before college began in the autumn. London was full of tourists.

We looked at all the famous buildings – Buckingham Palace, The Tower of London. And we went to restaurants and theatres in the evenings. It was interesting and exciting and I began to forget the bad times in Hong Kong.

'I'm pleased we came to London,' I told my mother.

But after a few weeks, she said, 'You need to find a college, Carol. You must go on studying. And I need a job.'

That evening, we looked in the newspapers.

'What about this?' I said. I showed my mother a job in the newspaper.

SECRETARY
for the summer months
on a small private island in Scotland.
Live with the family in a big house.
Interesting work and good pay
for the right person.

Phone Greta Ross. Telephone number 071 . . .

London was interesting and exciting, and I began to forget the bad times in Hong Kong.

'Well, that sounds interesting,' said my mother. 'I'd like to work as a secretary on an island in Scotland. It's a beautiful country, Carol, and you can go to a college there in the autumn.'

'And it's a place to live for the summer,' I said. 'Hotels are expensive.'

My mother telephoned Greta Ross.

'Come and see me tomorrow,' Greta Ross told her. 'Come to the Savoy Hotel at eleven o'clock.'

I went to the Savoy Hotel with my mother. It was big and expensive, bigger than our hotel, and in the centre of London.

'Mum needs this job,' I thought. 'And a private island in Scotland is a nice place to live. Perhaps I can forget what's happened if I go there.'

'Room twenty-two,' said the woman at the hotel desk. 'Go on up. Mrs Ross will see you now.'

Greta Ross was waiting for us. She was about thirty years old and very beautiful. She wore an expensive red dress and her hair was very long and dark.

'This is my daughter, Carol,' said my mother.

'Hallo, Carol,' said Greta Ross.

'Hallo,' I said.

'Carol is eighteen years old,' said my mother. 'Can she come with me, if I get the job? Perhaps she can help in the

Greta Ross was waiting for us.

house or in the gardens. She likes gardening. She's studying farming at college.'

'Perhaps,' said Greta Ross. 'There's a small farm on the island.'

'I'd like to work on the farm,' I said.

Greta Ross looked at my mother. 'How long did you live in Hong Kong, Mrs Sanders?'

'Seven years,' answered my mother. 'My husband died in a plane crash last year, so we've come back to live in England.'

'Where did you live before Hong Kong?'

'We lived in India for three years.'

Then Greta Ross took my mother into a room and asked her more questions. I waited outside.

'Greta Ross is nice,' I thought. 'I hope my mother gets the job.'

Soon after, the door opened and my mother came out. She was smiling.

Greta Ross said, 'Please wait here for a minute, Mrs Sanders. I want to make a phone call.' She went back into the room, and closed the door.

I was sitting on a chair near the door, and I could just hear Greta Ross's voice speaking on the phone.

'I think I've found someone,' she was saying. 'She has a daughter, but the girl can work in the garden or on the farm . . . Don't worry, they've been away from England for ten years . . . It'll be all right, I tell you . . . Don't worry.'

After a few minutes, Greta Ross put down the phone and came out of the room.

'You've got the job,' she told my mother.

My mother was pleased. 'Thank you,' she replied.

I was pleased, too, but now I was worried about that phone call. I didn't understand it.

I could just hear Greta Ross's voice speaking on the phone.

2

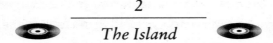

The Island

We went to Scotland the next day, first by plane, then by train. Greta Ross travelled with us.

I looked out of the train window and saw fields and villages and mountains. 'Mum is right,' I thought. 'Scotland is a very beautiful place.'

'You're going to be my husband's secretary,' Greta Ross told my mother. 'He's a businessman, but he never leaves the island. He does all his work by telephone and letter and computer. He invests money in companies, all over the world.'

'Do many people live on the island?' I asked.

'Not many,' said Greta Ross. 'You'll meet them soon.'

'Greta Ross is young,' I thought. 'Is her husband young, too? How can a young man buy an island? Is he very rich?'

After the train, we went on Mr Ross's boat, which took us out to the island. The boatman was a young man. He had dark hair and was brown from the sun.

'This is Tony,' said Greta Ross. 'He works for Mr Ross.'

'Hi,' said Tony.

Soon we were near the island. I could see the beaches and the cliffs. The boat slowed down.

'There are dangerous rocks around the island,' explained

Tony. 'A lot of them are under the water and you can't see them. I have to be careful. But the rocks keep other boats away, and that pleases Mr Ross.'

'Why?' I asked.

Tony looked at Greta Ross but she wasn't listening. 'Mr Ross doesn't like visitors to the island,' Tony said in a quiet voice.

Then Greta Ross looked at us and Tony said no more.

'Why doesn't Mr Ross like visitors?' I thought. 'Has he something to hide?'

When we arrived on the island, my mother and I followed Greta up to the house. It was very big and there were trees all around it.

A woman was waiting inside the house.

'This is Mrs Duncan, Tony's mother,' said Greta. 'She's the housekeeper and her husband is the gardener. Mrs Duncan will take you up to your rooms. I'm going to tell Mr Ross you've arrived.'

The housekeeper was a little woman with short hair. She went up the stairs, and my mother and I went after her.

My room was next to my mother's. I looked out of the window and saw the gardens at the back of the house. A man was working in the garden, near some trees. 'Is that Mr Duncan?' I thought. I looked between the trees and saw the sea. 'It's a beautiful house and a beautiful island.'

'Mr Ross doesn't like visitors to the island,' Tony said.

That evening, we had dinner with Mr and Mrs Duncan and Tony. We ate in the big kitchen.

'What happened to Mr Ross's last secretary?' asked my mother.

'She's in hospital,' replied Mrs Duncan. 'She's going to be away all summer.'

'Isn't Mrs Ross lonely here?' I said.

'No,' said Mrs Duncan. 'She likes painting a lot. She has a room upstairs and goes there to paint. She's very good. Sometimes she goes to different places on the island to paint pictures.'

We finished eating our meal. Soon after, Greta Ross came into the kitchen.

'Mr Ross wants to see you and your daughter now, Mrs Sanders,' she said. 'Follow me, please.'

We followed her through the house and into a big room. This was Mr Ross's office and he was sitting behind a desk.

I was surprised. He was a young man, about thirty. He had a moustache, short dark hair, and he wore glasses.

Mr Ross was speaking into the telephone. 'Who does he look like?' I thought. 'Is it Tony Duncan?'

'Mr Ross is talking to a business friend in New York,' said Greta. 'Please, sit down.'

While we waited, I looked around the office. There were three telephones, a computer, and lots of books and papers.

'Who does he look like?' I thought.

There was another door and I could see a smaller room, next to the office. There was a smaller desk and another computer in there.

Mr Ross finished speaking on the phone, then looked carefully at my mother and me. For a few seconds he didn't speak, and just watched us. Then he said, 'I'm pleased to meet you, Mrs Sanders. I need some help with my work. My secretary is in hospital, and there's a lot of work to do. Sometimes you'll have to work late at night, because of time differences in New York and Tokyo. Is that all right?'

'Yes, that's all right,' said my mother.

'Can you use a computer?'

'Yes.'

'Good.' He looked at me. 'Is this your daughter?'

'Yes, this is Carol,' said my mother.

'Hallo,' I said.

'Greta says you like gardening. There's a big garden here, so you can help Mr Duncan. And there's a farm. Dan and Stella Parks live in the farmhouse and work on the farm. You can help them, too. We have some animals. Some sheep, a few cows and chickens. And there's a horse called Smoke. He's grey, like his name. Can you ride?'

'Yes,' I said. 'I can ride a horse.'

'You can ride Smoke around the island, if you like.'

'I'd like that,' I said. 'Thank you.'

'And we grow vegetables and fruit,' he said. 'I work on the farm sometimes. I enjoy it.'

I smiled at him but he didn't smile back.

'Carol will enjoy working on the farm,' said my mother. 'Won't you, Carol?'

'Yes,' I said.

'Mr Ross looks sad,' I thought. 'But how did he get all his money? And why does he hide away on an island?'

3

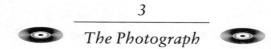

The Photograph

I worked in the garden for the first two days. The weather was hot and sunny. I liked working with Mr Duncan, and he was pleased with my work.

'You're a good gardener,' he said.

'I've always liked gardening,' I said. 'But I'm studying at college to be a farmer.'

Sometimes I saw Greta Ross.

'She likes to be alone,' I thought. Once or twice I saw Greta go out with her painting things. She went up on the hills or down to the beach.

Mr Duncan took me to the farm and I met Dan and Stella Parks. They were very friendly.

'You can work on the farm for the next three days,' said

18

Dan Parks. 'Mr Duncan says you're a good gardener. Are you a good farmer, too?'

I smiled at him. 'I am,' I said.

He smiled back.

So I worked on the farm with Mr and Mrs Parks. They were nice people. I helped with the cows and the chickens, and went up on the hills with Mr Parks and his dog to look at the sheep.

One afternoon I went out riding. Smoke was a big, lazy, friendly horse. I enjoyed riding and Smoke knew his way around the island very well. I learned new places to go to.

I rode along the cliff top and then in between some trees. When we came out of the trees, I saw the house from the other side. I tried to find the window of my room. Which one was it?

Suddenly, I saw a face at one of the windows. The face was looking at me. It was there for just a second or two, then it moved away quickly.

'Who was that?' I thought. 'Was it Mr Ross? And which room was it?'

I didn't see my mother very much that first week. She worked all day and in the evenings. She wrote letters to South America, Japan, Canada and Australia. Sometimes, she worked after I was in bed.

'Mr Ross works hard,' she told me. 'He invests money

Suddenly I saw a face at one of the windows.

in many companies and countries. But it's not his money.'

'It's not?' I was surprised by this.

'No, it's his wife's money. And she bought the island. It's her island, her house, her farm. Everything belongs to her.'

'How strange. But why does Mr Ross always look sad? And why does he never leave the island?' I asked.

'I don't know,' said my mother. 'He says he likes it here and likes working on his farm. It's strange, I know.'

Sometimes, when I finished work, I walked along the beaches or the cliffs. Or I went swimming in the sea. I liked swimming. Greta Ross often came to the beach to swim, but Mr Ross never came.

'Stay away from the rocks, Carol,' Greta Ross told me. 'They're very dangerous.'

'I will,' I said.

Sometimes I took my camera to the beach and took photographs of some of the boats that went by. I took photographs of the birds on the cliffs.

There were other small islands near our island, and boats with tourists stopped at them. But no boats stopped at our island. They kept away from the dangerous rocks. Tony was right. The island did not have visitors.

One day, I was walking back to the house, and had my camera with me. I stopped and looked at the big house.

Mr Duncan was working in the garden in front of it. At first, he didn't see me.

'I'm going to take a photograph of the house,' I thought. 'The sun is in just the right place, and it will make a good picture.'

I looked at the building through my camera, and took the photograph. Mr Ross was coming out of a door. He was in my picture, too, and he looked angry.

'That's all right,' I thought. 'It's still a good photograph.'

But Mr Duncan was running across the grass. He came quickly up to me and said, 'Give me your camera.' He looked very worried.

'What's wrong?' I asked in surprise. I gave him the camera.

'Never take photographs of Mr Ross,' he said. And then he opened the back of my camera and took out the film.

'Hey! What are you doing?' I said. 'You'll spoil my film!'

But he didn't stop. 'Sorry,' he said, and he put the film into his pocket. 'But no pictures of Mr Ross. He doesn't like people to take pictures of him.'

Mr Ross was watching us. He saw the camera and he saw Mr Duncan take out the film, but he said nothing. Then he turned and went back into the house.

Later, I told my mother about Mr Duncan and the camera. 'He spoiled my film,' I said.

'Hey! What are you doing?' I said. 'You'll spoil my film!'

'I don't understand,' she said. 'Why did he do that?'

'I don't know,' I said, 'but there's something strange about Mr Ross.'

About a week later, I finished work early one day and came back to the house. My mother was working in her small room, next to Mr Ross's office. Mrs Duncan was in the kitchen. Greta Ross was painting in her room upstairs.

I went to my room and began reading a book. I was sitting beside the window. After half an hour, I got tired of reading. I looked out at the rain, and the grey sea and rocks between the trees.

'My book isn't very interesting,' I thought.

I got up and went out of my room. I walked along the passage and turned a corner. Then I saw the door at the end of the passage. There was a large plant in a plant pot outside the door.

'Where does that door go?' I thought. 'I haven't seen it before.' I remembered the face at the window in my first week on the island. 'Perhaps it's the door to *that* room,' I thought.

I walked along to the door and turned the handle. The door didn't move. It was locked.

'What are you doing!' said a voice behind me.

I turned round quickly and saw Greta Ross. She looked angry.

Greta Ross looked angry. 'That room is private,' she said.

'That room is private,' she said.
'I'm sorry,' I said. 'I didn't—'
'Stay away from there,' she told me.

* * *

25

I told my mother about the locked door.

'What's behind it?' I said. 'Is it a secret?'

'I don't know,' said my mother. 'It doesn't matter. Mr Ross can have locked rooms if he wants them.'

'I think he does have secrets,' I said. 'There's something strange about him. There's something strange about this island. Somebody isn't telling us something. Something important.'

My mother laughed. 'Stop playing detective, Carol,' she said.

4

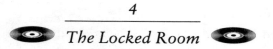 *The Locked Room*

*T*wo days later there was a storm in the middle of the night.

I was hot and I couldn't sleep. I got out of bed, went across to the window and looked out at the night. Black clouds hurried across the sky, and the trees moved wildly in the wind. The rain made a loud noise on the window.

I opened my window and put my head out into the wind and the rain. I looked at the other windows in the house. Most of them were dark. But one window had a light in it. 'Somebody isn't sleeping,' I thought. 'Which room is that?'

There were six windows between my window and the room with the light.

'And there are six doors between my room and the locked door!' I thought. 'That light is in the locked room. Somebody's in there!'

I put on my dressing-gown and went out of my room. The house was dark, and at first I couldn't see very well. I walked along the passage and turned the corner.

There it was, the locked room. And there was a light under the door!

I went nearer and heard noises.

'Somebody's moving about in the locked room,' I thought. 'Who is it?'

Then the light went off and the door opened.

I was afraid to move.

Somebody came out of the room, and into the dark passage. Lightning suddenly lit up the house, and I saw who it was.

'It's Mr Ross!' I thought. 'What was he doing in that room in the middle of the night?'

I didn't move and he didn't see me. He locked the door of the room carefully. He didn't put the key in his pocket, but hid it in the plant pot next to the door.

'He's coming along here,' I thought. 'I must get back to my room.'

And I ran back along the passage.

Mr Ross hid the key in the plant pot next to the door.

Mr Ross heard me. 'Who's that?' he called.

I didn't answer, but ran into my room and closed the door.

He came along the passage and stopped outside my door. Then he walked past and went on down the stairs.

I took off my dressing-gown and went back to bed. I was shaking because I was afraid.

'Now I know how to get into the locked room,' I thought. 'But what's in there?'

There was no storm in the morning, but it was still raining. I got up early and worked on the farm. There were eggs from the chickens and I put them in boxes. I helped to milk the cows and then took them out to the field.

Later, I went back into the house for breakfast. 'Did you sleep all right last night?' asked Mrs Duncan. 'Or did the storm wake you up?'

'I . . . slept all right,' I said. I didn't want to tell her about the light in the locked room, or about Mr Ross.

After breakfast, I went back upstairs. Mr Ross was talking on the telephone in his office. My mother was working at her desk. I knew that Mrs Duncan was in the kitchen and that Mr Duncan was working in the garden.

'Where's Mrs Ross?' I thought.

Then I looked out of the window and saw her with Tony Duncan. They were walking to the boat.

'He's taking her out in the boat,' I thought. 'Perhaps she's going to Edinburgh.'

The boat moved away from the island and I waited until it was out at sea. Then I opened the door of my room.

There was nobody in the passage and I ran along to the locked room. The key was still in the plant pot and I took it out. My hand was shaking.

Then I unlocked the door.

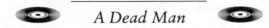

5

A Dead Man

I went into the room . . . and I was very surprised.
The room was full of strange things. Coloured shirts
and suits. Three guitars. And there were posters and
photographs on the walls.

I looked at the posters.

Jake Rosso's face looked down at me.

I looked at the dead Jake Rosso's picture, and I
remembered all the photographs on the walls of my room
in Hong Kong. I could never forget that face – the face of
my favourite singer.

Then, while I looked at his face, something strange happened. I began to see another face in the posters. An older face, and with a moustache, but the *same* face.

I saw the face of Mr Ross.

'No!' I said. 'It's not true!'

But it was, I knew it was.

'Mr Ross is . . . *Jake Rosso*!'

I looked at the dead Jake Rosso's picture – and I saw the face of Mr Ross!

31

'No!' said a voice behind me.

I turned round and saw Mr Ross. He was standing in the doorway. He looked . . . afraid.

'I don't believe you!' I said.

'You have to believe me!'

I looked at the posters. 'Who is that, if it's not you?'

'It's Jake Rosso. He was . . . my brother.'

'That's not true!' I shouted. 'I don't believe you. Listen, Jake Rosso was my favourite singer – I had hundreds of photos of him. I still have all his records. I *loved* him, do you understand? Thousands of people loved him.'

'He's dead,' Mr Ross said quietly.

'*No!*' I shouted. 'You're Jake Rosso! You look different now, yes. You've got short hair, you've got a moustache now, and you wear glasses. But you're . . . Jake . . . Rosso. You were my favourite pop star, so I *know*.'

Mr Ross said nothing, and watched my face.

'He doesn't know what to do,' I thought. 'He knows I don't believe him, and he's afraid.'

Then he said, 'It was you in the passage last night, wasn't it?'

'Yes,' I answered.

He looked angry. 'I was wrong to give your mother a job,' he said. 'I thought it was OK because you came from Hong Kong. And I needed help with my work. I needed a good secretary.'

32

'You're Jake Rosso!' I shouted.

'Does your other secretary know who you are?' I asked.
'Do the other people on the island know?'

Mr Ross didn't answer, but walked across to the
window. He was thinking.

33

'What's he going to do?' I thought.

Then he turned round. 'OK, you're right. I . . . I am Jake Rosso.'

'I *knew* it!'

He looked worried and unhappy. 'Can you keep a secret? A very important secret?'

I thought for a minute, then I said, 'Yes, I can keep a secret.'

Then he told me.

'The other people on this island are my family.'

'Your family?' I said.

'Yes. My real name is James Duncan, and Mr and Mrs Duncan are my father and mother. Tony is my younger brother, and his wife, Lisa, is my secretary. It's she who's in hospital.'

'And Dan and Stella Parks?' I asked.

'My mother's sister and her husband,' he said.

'But what are you doing here on this island? I don't understand.'

'I'll tell you,' he said. He sat down on a chair and took a guitar in his hands, but he didn't play it. 'You were right. I was a famous pop star. I was very rich, and I had a beautiful wife. But things went wrong.'

'How?'

'I took drugs,' he said. 'I drank a lot of alcohol. I got drunk and crashed cars. I did stupid, terrible things. I

knew it was wrong but I couldn't stop doing it. I was
. . . crazy, for a time.'

'I can understand that,' I told him. 'I've taken drugs,
too.'

He looked surprised. 'You have?'

'Yes,' I said. 'After my father died, I was very unhappy
and things went wrong for me too. But go on with your
story.'

He went on. 'One night, I was driving my car. I was
drunk and – and I hit somebody. A young girl. She . . .
died. I killed her.'

'Oh, no!'

'Yes,' he said. 'She was fifteen years old. I wanted to
die, too. The money didn't matter any more. Nothing
mattered any more.'

'What did you do after the accident?' I asked.

'I drove on in the car. I didn't stop, and I didn't tell the
police. I had killed someone and I was afraid.' He looked
afraid now. He put the guitar down and went on with his
story. 'So I made a plan. Jake Rosso had to die, too. It was
the best thing to do. And so . . . I "killed" him.'

'But you're still alive.'

'My family know I'm alive, but no other people know.'
He looked at me. 'But now *you* know.'

'How did you do it?' I asked.

'I told my family about my plan and I told Greta, my

'I hit a young girl, and she died. I killed her.'

wife. At first they didn't like it. But after a long time, they said OK. Then I faked the car crash.'

'*Faked* it?'

'Yes,' he said. 'I put some of my things in the car. A guitar, and some clothes. Then I pushed my car over a cliff and burned it. The police found the burned car and thought I was dead. Everybody thought I was killed in the car crash.'

'But you faked the crash,' I said.

'Yes.'

'What did you do then?'

'My family hid me away for months. I tried to change into a different person – shorter hair, a moustache, quiet suits. All my money went to Greta and she changed her name to Ross. I told her to buy this island. Now I invest her money, the money that was mine. And now I'm "James Ross".'

'What about "Jake Rosso"?' I asked.

'Jake Rosso took drugs,' he said. 'Jake Rosso got drunk and crashed cars. He killed a young girl, so he had to "die". I can never forget the girl. I think about her every day.'

'And that's why you always look so sad,' I thought.

I looked around the room. 'Why do you keep a room like this? Why do you keep the guitars, the posters and photographs?'

'Everybody thought I was killed in the car crash.'

James Ross did not speak for a minute. Then he said, 'I need to remember my old life, and what Jake Rosso was like. I'm never going to sing again and I'm never going to take drugs. But I need this room, to remember.'

I looked at the posters and the photographs. And I looked at his sad face. 'I'm not going to say anything. I won't tell my mother, I won't tell anybody.'

James Ross looked at me. 'I think you understand,' he said.

'I do,' I said. 'I've done bad things. I want to forget them, too. I needed to get away, to hide, too. That's why we came to England, to begin a new life. Yes, I understand.'

He took my hand, and we walked out of the room and closed the door.

I never went into the room again, and I didn't tell anybody.

My mother and I left the island at the end of the summer. Soon after, I went to college.

My life is better now. I work on a farm in England and my mother works in an office. My mother doesn't worry about me, because I'm happier now.

I haven't been back to the island.

But I know there's a 'dead man' living there.

I haven't been back to the island. But I know there's a 'dead man' living there.

Exercises

A   Checking your understanding

Chapter 1 *Write answers to these questions.*

1   How did Carol's father die?
2   How old was Carol when her father died?
3   Why did Carol stop working at college?
4   What did Carol begin to do with her new friends?
5   Why did Carol want to come back to England?
6   Where did Carol and her mother meet Greta Ross?

Chapter 2 *Who said or thought these words?*

1   'How can a young man buy an island?'
2   'Mr Ross doesn't like visitors to the island.'
3   'Mr Ross is talking to a business friend in New York.'
4   'My secretary is in hospital and there's a lot of work to do.'
5   'Carol will enjoy working on the farm.'

Chapter 3 *Are these sentences true (T) or false (F)?*

1   Dan and Stella Parks were not very friendly to Carol.
2   Smoke knew his way around the island.
3   The island belonged to Mr Ross.
4   Carol took a photograph of Mr Ross.
5   Mr Ross took the film out of the camera.

Chapter 4 *Who in this chapter . . .*

1   . . . was hot and couldn't sleep?
2   . . . was in the locked room?
3   . . . went out in the boat?

Chapter 5 *Find answers to these questions.*

1   What was Mr Ross's real name?
2   Who were Mr and Mrs Duncan?
3   How old was the girl who was killed in Jake Rosso's car accident?
4   How did Jake Rosso fake his death?
5   When did Carol leave the island?

B Working with language

1 *Complete these sentences with information from the story.*

1 Carol was very unhappy after . . . . .
2 The police didn't arrest Carol but she . . . . .
3 Carol's mother needed a job so . . . . .
4 Mr Ross needed a new secretary because . . . . .
5 When Carol took her photo of the house, Mr Ross . . . . .
6 Mr Duncan took the film out of the camera because . . . . .
7 Mr Ross locked the door of the room carefully and . . . . .
8 When Mr Ross called 'Who's that?', Carol . . . . .

2 *Put these sentences in the right order. Check your order with Chapter 5.*

1 He didn't tell the police about the accident because he was afraid.
2 When the police found the burned car, they thought Jake Rosso was dead.
3 When Jake Rosso was driving his car one night, he had an accident.
4 After some months Greta changed her name to Ross and bought the island with Jake's money.
5 He hit a young girl and she died.
6 So he put a guitar and some clothes in his car.
7 Now Mr Ross lives very quietly but he can never forget the young girl who died.
8 At the same time Jake Rosso changed into Mr James Ross, a businessman.
9 Then he pushed the car over a cliff and burned it.
10 He decided that Jake Rosso had to die, too.

C Activities

1 You are Carol in the story. Write a letter to a friend and explain why you think there is something strange about Mr Ross.
2 You are a newspaper reporter. Write a report about Jake Rosso's death in a car crash.
3 Jake Rosso has just come home after the accident when he killed a young girl. He tells his wife, Greta, about the accident and about his plan to fake his own death. Write down their conversation.
4 Write a letter to the author of the book and say what you like and don't like about it.

Glossary

alcohol drinks like beer, wine, whisky, etc.

arrest when the police catch someone and take them to prison

ate past tense of 'to eat'

been past participle of 'to be'

began past tense of 'to begin'

bought past tense of 'to buy'

came past tense of 'to come'

care (didn't care) to feel that something is (not) interesting or (not) important

cliff the high, steep side of a hill

college a place where people go to study after they leave school

company a number of people who work together in business

computer a machine that holds information and works out answers

could past tense of 'can'

crazy mad; very stupid

cried past tense of 'to cry'

done past participle of 'to do'

drank past tense of 'to drink'

dressing-gown a warm coat to put over night clothes

drove past tense of 'to drive'

drugs dangerous things that people eat or smoke or put into their body

drunk *(adj)* when somebody cannot walk or talk clearly after drinking too much alcohol

fake *(v)* to make or do something that looks real but is not real

farm a place where you grow food and keep animals

found past tense of 'to find'

glasses round pieces of glass that you wear over the eyes to see better

got past tense of 'to get'

had past tense of 'to have'

handle *(n)* the part of a door that you hold to open it

heard past tense of 'to hear'

housekeeper a person who looks after a house

hid past tense of 'to hide'

invest to put money into a business and get more money back later

kept past tense of 'to keep'

knew past tense of 'to know'